The Plucky Orangutan

Written by Catherine Veitch Illustrated by Elissambura

Miles Kelly

Oma the orangutan wanted to be good at everything. She loved trying new things.

Every waking hour, when she was not eating or napping, she loved doing challenges.

One day, Oma's friend Amir challenged her to build the best tree nest.

"It will be the cosiest nest any orangutan has ever made!" said Oma, as she gathered branches with the biggest, softest leaves to line her new nest.

But... **Whoosh**... a rain cloud burst overhead! Rain flooded into Oma's nest and quickly soaked the leaves, and Oma.

"I wish you would **GO AWAY!**" Oma shouted at the rain. "Look at my soggy bottom! I'm not the best at building a cosy nest."

"Why don't you try building a nest in the fastest time instead?" said Amir, as he sheltered under a giant leaf.

RAIN GO AWAY!

Word spread about Oma's next challenge and when the rain stopped, she was ready to begin. Vina, who was the fastest nest-builder many years ago, counted Oma down...

"One, two, three, orangutan-go!"

The sounds of bend... snap, bend... snap echoed around the forest as Oma whipped branches off the trees. But the branches were wet and slimy, and many slipped out of her hands.

"Time's up!" shouted Vina. "Stop what you're doing."

Oma did not feel confident with this challenge either.

"Can you stand up in your nest?" shouted one of the watching orangutans.

Oma nervously stepped in.
But... her nest was not
very strong!

"I'm not the best at building
nests in super-quick time
either," said Oma sadly.

Amir suggested that for Oma's
next challenge, she could try
building the highest nest.

Oma bravely climbed the tallest tree she could find. She could see for miles!

"It's windy up here!" she nervously shouted down. But she would not give up the challenge.

"I CAN do this," she told herself.

Amir was not so sure about the view when he joined Oma.

"Look, the rain clouds are coming back!"

I have the best view over the forest!

Oma and Amir scrambled down just in time, as heavy rain washed Oma's nest away.

"My idea to build a nest that high was not so great!" said Amir, as leaves and branches fell on Oma's head.

"The rain has destroyed ALL of my nests.
I wish it never rained," said Oma.
But Oma, the rain is important to our forest.

Oma did not believe Amir. The two friends carried on arguing and were getting wetter and wetter.

"I challenge you to prove that plants need the rain," said Oma. "Let's have a competition!"

When it stopped raining, Amir was ready to take up Oma's challenge. Vina volunteered to judge the competition and gave each of them a young tree to plant.

It did not take Amir long to find
the perfect spot to plant his tree.

"Here my sapling will have shelter, light, and the
rain will drip off that leaf and water it," he said.

Oma found it much harder to find a spot for her
tree. But eventually she found a dry tree hollow
that did not have any animals in.

After a week it was time to check on the young trees. First they all went to Amir's sapling.

"I don't believe it!" Amir beamed. "My sapling has grown five more leaves!"

Then they went to look at Oma's sapling. Sadly, her small tree had not grown any more leaves.

But Oma was still hopeful. "Perhaps it's a slow starter, like me!" she said.

After two weeks it was time for the final check. Amir's sapling had grown tall and strong.

"I knew the rain would help my tree to grow!" boasted Amir.

But Oma's sapling looked very sorry for itself. It had wilted and withered. This was another challenge that Oma had not won.

"Now do you believe me?" asked Amir.

Yes, I agree,
our forest needs the
rain to grow.

Oma was sad. "I'm not the best at building nests or growing a tree."

"But you are the best at something," said Vina. Oma could not think of anything she was good at.

"Everytime something went wrong, you kept trying and you never gave up," smiled Vina. "You are the best at trying your best."

The End